RIDE / SHARE

MICHAEL ESTRIN

CONTENTS

1

AN OPEN BOOK

"You're going to my part of town," the Lyft driver says. "I live around the corner from Cedars Sinai."

"I love that neighborhood. Great walking."

"Oh yes. I walk everywhere, so I know everyone."

We stumble into a tangent about his neighbor, George, who went senile and may have kicked off a hyper-local trend of wearing bathrobes to the Beverly Center. But eventually, the conversation comes back to the bottom line.

"I pay $650 a month for a one-bedroom."

"Holy shit," I say.

"Of course, I've been there twenty years, but you can still pick your spots. I know one lady, it's impolite to say it, but she waits for people around us to die, and she buys up the property."

I think about that old *Seinfeld* joke about combining the obits with the real estate section, but all I can say is "oh."

"Of course, there's karma. You know what that is? What goes around comes around. So now she's dying and her son is waiting her out."

He laughs about it, and so I force a laugh too.

There's traffic going over Laurel, so we get some backstory. He was born in LA, but he lived in Europe for twenty years in the seventies and eighties. He was a photographer, mostly fashion and advertising.

"I went to Sweden for three days, and I ended up staying five years. I joined a ski club. I used to hang out with the king on his yacht. He was a crazy fellow . . . just one of those guys, you know . . . too much money. Anyway, I had a great time in Sweden. I think I was the only black guy in the whole country. I tried to recruit my friends to come, but they just thought it was cold, which it was. You know, not a lot of black people ski."

But then he left Sweden for Germany.

"I met a woman, and three weeks later we were married."

"Wow. You move fast."

"Let me tell you something. Men think they're the ones making the move. Wrong. Women choose us. They have the power."

We stumble into another tangent, this one about his friend the brain surgeon, who he met through Quincy Jones. Then, at the Mulholland light, as if it's the most natural thing in the world, he hands me his book.

"These are my photos. Pretty much the story of my life."

I open the book. There's a portrait of the artist as a young man.

"That was me in elementary school in Germany. I was an Army brat before Dad retired in LA. That girl there with the freckles, I was in love with her. My wife had freckles. I used to count them every night— 113 freckles. First time I saw her, with those freckles, I thought she was the girl from elementary school."

I turn the page. The photos look like paintings shrouded in fog.

"That's a technique I invented."

"How'd you do it?"

"Marijuana."

I burst out laughing.

"No, but it's true. I smoked a joint, spent nine hours in the darkroom, and that's what came out. Of course, back in those days even little old ladies smoked grass. Take a look at this canyon."

He points out the window at Laurel Canyon. The mountains appear to kiss the sky. The ravines plunge down at impossible angles.

"You could drive through here and get high, thick as the smoke was in those days," he continues. "And the cops didn't hassle, because these were hippies who had good lawyers."

I flip through the book. His work is beautiful. I stop on a black-and-white photo of a man wearing a suit, sprawled out in an inner tube on a pond. The man puffs on a cigar.

"He was my partner. A really crazy German. Family money. He used to break the dishes because they were dirty. His father's generation murdered their father before he could disinherit them."

"Murder?"

"It happens. I met the dad. This was before I knew about the murder. He seemed crazy like a character. He had a beautiful wife and an ugly mistress. Makes no sense. Anyway, I ask what he does, and he won't tell. OK. But then he takes me aside and says he will tell, but I need to keep it secret. OK. So he's a spy, he says. I've never met a spy. All I know is the spies in the TV shows, so I say, for who? And he says, I haven't decided yet. Well, once I heard about the murder, I got the hell away. And I told my partner, you hang around long enough and you'll end up like him. These are people with too much money, you know, and they just go funny in the head."

I look at the picture again. I notice the man's devilish smile bathed in a halo of light.

"You really captured him. You have a great eye."

"It's not the eye. It's my ear. I hear a great story and do my best to find it in their face."

I turn the page. It's a fashion model from the eighties. I don't know her name, but she looks vaguely familiar. She is stunning.

"What's her story?" I ask.

"Cocaine."

I know there's got to be more to that story, and more tangents involving record producers and royals and fashion-forward bathrobe trends, but we have reached my destination.

"I hope I didn't talk too much," he says.

"Not at all."

"Yeah, I figured the way you were taking notes with your eyes that you were probably a story guy."

He has read me like a book, and, returning his book, I suppose I have done the same.

2

EIGHTY HOOKERS

Last night's Lyft driver has a glowing pink mustache on his dash. He offers water, candy, or gum. He's a pro. We chat, and soon I learn that he's been driving for two years and that he's writing a book about LA's after-dark crowd.

"I've driven eighty hookers," he explains.

"Wow! That's a lot of hookers. And you're taking notes, yes?"

"Of course."

Like I said, he's a pro.

"So . . . what's the craziest story?" I ask.

"It's not about a hooker."

"That's OK, not every story has to have a hooker."

"Well, a couple had sex in my car once," he says.

I swivel to inspect the backseat.

"No offense," I say, "but your car is kind of small for that."

"I *know!*"

He explains that he picked up the couple outside of a strip club, but he knew she wasn't a stripper because he drives all the strippers. Less than a minute after he started driving, he heard the seat belts come off.

"It was a short ride," he explains. "So I'm like, they're going to make out. I don't want them to take the seat belts off, but we're just a few minutes away, and I just don't want to have a confrontation, because sometimes those happen and they're just . . . not good."

"OK."

"But then I heard moaning and I looked in the mirror, and things were . . . rhythmic."

"Unreal."

"Yeah. And I'm just thinking, crap, now I gotta go get my car steam cleaned, so my night's done."

"So they finished before you got to the destination?"

"No! They just kept going!"

"So you said something?"

"I set the parking brake really loud and cleared my throat. Then I put on the dome light."

"And that stopped them?"

"Nope."

"Sheesh."

"So then I thought, maybe they just need a minute."

"So, you waited for them to finish?"

"I waited for them to finish."

"How long?"

"I just counted to sixty and then I said something."

"Like stop fucking in my car?"

"Actually, it was 'You're here!'"

"That was probably more diplomatic."

"Yup."

"And that worked?"

"Yup."

We arrive at my destination. I exit, but before we part, I tell him he has a good story for his book.

"Can't use it."

"Why not?"

"Dude, I have eighty stories about hookers. The title is I *Drove Eighty Hookers*."

"Not every story has to be about hookers," I remind him.

3

MUSIC TO MY EARS

The Lyft driver doesn't want to talk. He wants to ROCK.

He snaps.

He whistles.

He sings along.

The steering wheel isn't just a mechanism for guiding the car, it's a drum.

Welcome to the Jungle

Sweet Home Alabama

You Spin Me Round

A View to a Kill

I Want You to Want Me

The only way to stop the music is to exit the vehicle. But there's *No Sleep Till Brooklyn*, and we've got a thing called *Radar Love*.

4

LANGUAGE BARRIER

I ask my Lyft driver how his day is going, but instead of answering that question, he informs me that he does not speak English very well.

We drive in silence for a stretch.

Eventually, we stop at a light. A jogger passes us. The man is shirtless and his torso is thick with sweat. My driver points and says, "Too hot, too stupid."

I agree that it's a little warm in the Valley for a mid-day run.

Later, when another car cuts us off, my driver points and says, "Big asshole."

No argument there.

Finally, we arrive at my apartment.

"Home sweet home," my driver says.

I thank him for the ride and tell him his English skills are a lot better than he thinks.

5

ELECTION NIGHT, 2016

The driver asks me what I think of this "crazy-ass election."

We've been stuck in traffic on the 101 for a while, and I've learned a few things about the man from South Bay:

He's originally from Atlanta but hasn't been back there since his mom passed. "Mom loved her flowers."

He drives for "milkshake money."

His "real job" is driving an 18-wheeler. The last load was hats; the one before that was Cup Noodles.

He mostly listens to hip hop, but "some country is good."

His feet are "too big for cowboy boots."

And here we are talking politics in traffic, a dicey proposition with a stranger in a "crazy-ass" election year.

"Hillary has some shit going with the FBI," he says. "But she's going to win because that's how they want it. Above the law."

They are the elite and they call the shots. The people who lead the elites are really lizards, and "they all went to Yale, or that other school."

The way he heard it, Bill Clinton is "dead set" on beating Wilt Chamberlain's record for sleeping with women. But he's not sure the former president will catch up to the former NBA star, because Bill is "only at, like, two thousand or something, and you know Wilt hit ten thousand."

He fears for Donald Trump's life.

"They'll take him out because they don't want him. He's just like Kennedy: for the people, so they'll kill him."

Kennedy loved his LSD. "Of course, he got with a lot of women too."

"Marilyn Monroe!" I offer.

"Men can't keep it zipped up," he says.

"That doesn't speak very highly of us," I say.

"You're right about that. "It's a whole new world order coming in, unless Trump can stop it, but they'll kill him if he tries, so . . ."

"What about Bernie?"

"I like that Bernie cat. But he has no experience. That's why it's Hillary. The elites have had a conspiracy for years to make her president."

"You really believe that?"

"Sure do," he says. "Who'd you vote for?"

I tell him I voted for her.

"No shit."

We share a chuckle.

"So you voted for Trump?"

"I wanted to, but I couldn't find the polling place, so I said fuck it."

Talk turns to basketball and how nobody in LA cares about the finals because the Lakers missed the playoffs.

6

FOREIGN

The Lyft driver begins his day at four a.m.

"Airport runs," he explains. "I work early morning to early evening because I don't like dealing with drunks."

"Some drivers tell me there's good money in drunk people," I say.

"That's true. But if they're not getting sick, they're trying to jump out of the car or something. And now there are the Trump supporters."

"What do they do?"

"They yell at me and tell me to go back to my country. Or they threaten to have me deported or to mess me up. It's how they feel, I guess, but they say these things because they're drunk, so that gives them the courage to call me racist names."

"What do you do?"

"Well, they're drunk. So I say, 'Why don't you be the DJ?' and I give them control of the radio. That usually works. Just distract them, you know. Change the topic."

"Where are you from?"

"Iran."

"Do the people who yell at you know where you're from?"

"No. They make assumptions. They say you are an Arab and that's that. Of course, I am not an Arab; I am Persian. They don't know the difference. One man accused me of plotting 9/11."

"That's crazy."

"Of course it's crazy. And he has no idea who he's talking to."

"How do you mean?"

"The second plane to hit the World Trade Center—I was supposed to be on that flight, but I missed my connection."

He explains how there was a mistake with his ticket, how he was turned away at the gate, how he felt so annoyed, and then hours later, how he broke down crying. Tears of joy that he was alive, tears of sorrow for the people killed.

"It messed with my head for months," he says.

"You're a better man than me. I don't think I'd ever get over that."

"We are more resilient than we think we are. But did you know I wasn't the only Persian crying that day?"

"What do you mean?"

"Back home people shed tears for the victims. Some people held vigils. Some of them were arrested for doing that, because the government says America is the enemy. But most people in Iran know better. They know the difference between the government and the country. People know that here too, even the Trump supporters who yell at me."

"Then why do you think they yell at you?"

"There's money in hate and fear. They don't see that they're being manipulated to think about people over there as the enemy because their government wants them to be afraid, wants them to be angry, so they will go along with whatever the government says. That's why you don't hear about dissent in Iran."

"It doesn't fit the narrative."

"Exactly."

We arrive at my destination.

"I've done thousands of rides. I don't normally talk to people about this—too dangerous. But I thought you would understand."

"Thank you for trusting me."

"Can you do me a favor?"

"Sure."

"You have a voice in this country."

"Yes."

"Please use it."

7

KARMA

It's rush hour, and the Lyft driver stops to let another motorist out of a parking lot and onto Laurel.

"It's a karma thing," she says.

So far, we've done the usual chitchat. She just started her shift. She likes the dinner/bar crowd. She prefers coffee, but 5-hour Energy will do in a pinch. Her dog is named Chill.

We cross Ventura and make the climb up the canyon. We move up the hill at a decent pace, but as we near Mulholland, traffic slows as two lanes merge into one. She needs to merge left, but she's running out of time and space, and if she can't merge, we'll be sent in the wrong direction, miles out of our way.

"Oh man, I hate being this person."

Things look ugly. I know she's just trying to merge. But from a distance, it looks as if she waited until the last possible moment in order to cut the line.

Will someone let her in?

Probably not. Not in this town.

Then a break in the traffic. She slides left like a boss, even blocking for another motorist trying to get right.

"That karma really paid off," I say.

She agrees. We chat about Waze. She loves it. She gives me her take on Uber versus Lyft.

We cross Mulholland. The traffic slows to a crawl as we make our way down the canyon.

"I was in West Hollywood one night, it was pop-ping—well, it's always popping. And I picked up this guy who wanted to go to Sunset. He wanted McDonald's."

She shrugs.

"There wasn't a lot of traffic. There was this girl walking down the street. She was wobbling around in the street. So I pulled over and said you got to get out of the road."

The girl was drunk, but intent on driving. The Lyft driver talked her out of the street, but maybe not out of driving.

"I wish I had grabbed her keys or something, but I couldn't really do anything. If I didn't have a rider, I would've just driven her."

She hopes the girl made it home safe. She laments the fact that the rider calls the shots, and he wanted to go to McDonald's ASAP.

Then she tells me about an accident she witnessed a couple of weeks ago. A reckless driver ran another motorist off the road and into a tree. This time, she stopped.

"We had to."

Her riders, a couple out for dinner, ran to the driver. She ran for the man's dog, who had been thrown from the car.

Neither man nor dog made it.

After the police arrived, she took the couple home, told them she'd wait if they wanted to change their clothes and try to salvage their night. They said no.

"The cop lives near me, out by Acton. I take the 14 in. You know how the cops live way out? So we're basically neighbors. I had been seeing him at the gym for years."

She bumps into him at the gym. The cop says the reckless driver got away.

"No cameras, no license plate."

"He got away?"

"That man and his dog are just gone. It's so sad, you know? So much damage because one guy just doesn't even think about anyone but himself."

We cross Sunset. We pass the McDonald's. We talk about the weather, we reach my destination. She is a good Lyft driver and a truly decent person. She waits for me to wave, so she knows I got in OK.

8

ADVICE FOR THE YOUNG DRIVER

A Nissan cuts us off.

"C'mon, you're better than that, man!" the driver shouts. His tone is friendly, like a coach urging you on after a busted play.

I show him a shortcut to Laurel. He explains his philosophy: ask everyone to do just a little better.

He likes the shortcut. "Pretty scenery, no traffic."

Near Mulholland, he asks what I do for a living. After the usual follow-ups, he asks if I'm happy.

"Yes. Most days. And on the worst days I can't imagine doing something else."

Here's his dilemma: he's a teacher's aide for developmentally disabled children. He likes his job, but he doesn't know if that's what he wants to do forever. He's twenty-two.

"Two cents from a guy pushing forty?" I ask.

"Please!"

"You can't predict the future," I say. "Most of my friends have reinvented their careers at least once."

"But they figured it out?"

"No. Not all of them. Some people need two or three things before they figure it out, and some people are still figuring it out."

"Oh, my god, that's what's totally freaking me out. What do you do about it?"

"Nothing. I mean, you try to find a job you like and you just keep checking in with yourself to make sure you're not becoming a miserable asshole. But basically you live your life and you learn to get comfortable knowing that most things are beyond your control."

"Wow, I'd love to be able to get to that place with everything I worry about."

"Me too."

9

KNOCKOUT

The Lyft driver says he has given more than eighty-five hundred rides on the platform.

"No way," I say.

"No joke, bro."

"Well, I guess you would have the data to back it up."

"Oh, I have the data."

"You must have some crazy stories."

"Like you would not believe."

"Try me."

"The thing is, 99 percent of the people are good people, nice people. You understand? They want a safe ride and a good chat, so we're in business, as they say."

He explains how he came to America six years ago from India, how he enjoys learning about his new country from the people he drives, and how he's never once experienced any kind of hatred because he's an immigrant.

"Not once, bro," he insists. "But there are some people, a very small group, who . . . they are entitled, OK? With them, it is like I don't exist because I am their servant. I am nothing to them, bro."

He tells me about a drunk woman who passed out in his car.

"She could not walk, so I had to get her inside. I carried her."

"You carried her?"

"Up three flights of stairs, bro. Then she got inside her apartment and she went right to the floor. I couldn't leave her there, so I carried her to the couch."

"Wow."

"Then I took photos of where I had been in her apartment, of her purse where I left it, and of her on the couch, sleeping safely."

"Why did you do that?"

"I have to protect myself. A criminal does not photograph a crime scene and send it to the authorities. I took the photos and sent them to Lyft immediately so they would have a record."

His logic is good and I'm impressed he had the presence of mind to document the situation, so I ask how he knew to do that.

"It is a common thing, bro. I've carried a lot of drunk passengers to their doors or inside. It has happened to all the drivers I know, so we have an unofficial procedure, understand?"

"Wow. That's nuts."

"If they are drinking too much, that is like a warning there could be a problem."

"Like the drunk Taco Bell executive who punched a driver?"

"Yes! You have seen this video?"

"Yes. That guy was an asshole."

"Yes! An asshole. That is why I have the dashboard camera. A police officer told me, anyone starts acting rude, turn it on just to be safe."

"But you've never had anyone get violent?"

"Oh yes, I have. You will laugh at the reason. He wanted me to drive him to Jack in the Box, go to the drive-thru, and pay for his meal because he did not have cash."

"And that got violent?"

"Yes. Because I refused, so he began hitting me. I got out of the car and opened his door to get him out, but he kept hitting me."

"What did you do?"

"I said, 'Sir, you must stop this.'"

"Did he stop?"

"No. He took another swing. I ducked underneath his swing, and I punched him. I knocked him out."

"One punch?"

"I am an amateur boxer," he says, pointing to a pair of miniature boxing gloves hanging from the mirror.

"Wow."

"Yes, my coach gave me the gloves, like a deterrent, but I do not think this passenger saw them, because he did not really see *me*, you understand?"

"I understand. What happened with the guy?"

"Oh, bro, it's a sick joke. I took him to the hospital because he was knocked out. I called the police to be safe. They said, it's not your fault, basically he is a drunk asshole. But I don't want to press charges; live and let live, that's how it goes."

"I feel a 'but' coming on."

"Yes, a but. Here is the but: he sues Uber and they ban me from the platform. So now I only drive Lyft—eight thousand five hundred rides, 4.9-star average."

"Wow, you really do have the data."

"I have the data, bro."

10

TRAVIS

The Lyft driver is named Travis. He says he has it all figured out. He's twenty-two.

"I graduated with a journalism degree," he explains. "But then I was like: fuck journalism. Because people can't accept the fact that quality news means you have to pay for it, so journalism is dead."

"So what's the plan now?"

"Hollywood," Travis says. "That's why I moved here from Kansas."

"Well, you're not in Kansas anymore," I say.

He laughs and compliments me on the *Swingers* reference, but he doesn't seem to know that *Swingers* was referencing *The Wizard of Oz*, which is a strange detail to miss because Mike and Trent met up with a "Dorothy" after the blackjack fiasco. Whatever.

"So you want to be an actor?" I ask.

"No way, man. Do I look like an actor?"

"What's an actor look like?"

"Chris Hemsworth."

"Good answer."

"I want to direct," Travis says.

"Big blockbuster movies?"

"That'd be cool, but studios are basically dead. It's all DIY stuff."

"So you got an idea for a movie?" I ask.

"Yeah, it's about a Lyft driver who isn't quite right in the head and he just drives around getting angry at shit, and then eventually he just explodes and shoots someone."

"I think I've seen that movie, Travis. It's called *Taxi Driver*."

"Man, like I told you, it's about a Lyft driver, because taxis are dead."

"Just like journalism."

"Exactly."

11

TECHNICAL DIFFICULTIES

We are experiencing technical difficulties.

The map and the pin have gone kerflooey. The Lyft driver is in the alley behind the building. I am on the street out in front of the building.

I call. Soon we have things sorted.

As we get underway, I admit that it may have been user error. But he graciously blames Google.

"Honestly, I'm just glad you didn't yell at me," he says. "Most people are so angry if they have to call."

He's not complaining. But I'm curious, so I ask.

The gist of his beef is this: there are too many people who think that you're their "bitch" because you have a service job.

"I'm still a person," he says.

"What kind of work would you like?" I ask.

He has a second job at a warehouse. He likes that job, but it doesn't pay enough to cover his bills.

"I just want a weekend," he says.

An oncoming motorcycle zigs and zags for no reason at all. The Lyft driver slows to give the biker a wide berth.

"What's up with this wingding?" I ask.

"He thinks he can't get hurt."

"That never ends well," I say.

"Nobody ever thinks the bad thing will happen to them."

"Yeah."

"What do you do for a living?" he asks. "You look like a writer."

"I am a writer. How did you get that?"

"Your hair. It's big and crazy. Beard. Glasses. Usually, that's either a writer or a computer programmer. But I knew you weren't a computer programmer . . ."

"Because of the screw-up with the map?" I ask.

He nods yes.

12

CULTURAL ADAPTATION

My Lyft driver is Gary. He tells me driving people around "kind of sucks."

It's not that Gary dislikes his passengers; he'd just rather do something else.

Gary explains that he used to be a sushi chef.

We talk about how there are a "crazy" number of sushi places on Ventura Boulevard and how the California roll is the "granddaddy" of "bullshit sushi rolls."

Gary attributes the popularity of "bullshit" sushi to the tastes of white people, which he describes as "not adventurous." But when he asks where I go for sushi, he nods approvingly at my answers.

"My dream," Gary says with a bashful smile, "is to open a restaurant someday."

"Sushi?" I ask, thinking that Gary's prior experience and strong opinions on the topic would make sushi the logical choice.

"Are you kidding, man? I'm Filipino. I will open a Filipino restaurant."

I tell Gary that's a great idea because there aren't a lot of Filipino restaurants in the Valley.

"Right! But there are a lot of Filipinos."

I tell Gary that he needs to think big, go after all the people in the area.

"Do you think white people will eat Filipino food?" he asks.

"Sure."

Gary ponders this for a moment. Actually, he ponders a little too long and we miss our chance to turn left at the light.

Eventually, he agrees that Filipino food could be a hit with white people, as long as he has some fried dishes on the menu.

"Exactly," I say. "Like how there are all those tempu-ra rolls. They make raw fish accessible."

"Tempura rolls," Gary sighs. "They are not sushi."

We drive the rest of the way in silence.

13

REFERENCES, DUDE

After an ambitious but legal U-turn, I tell the Lyft driver that he clearly knows his way around these crazy streets.

"Dude," he says. "Driving has been my side hustle from day one. I used to drive town cars."

"Why'd you switch?"

"The hours," he says. "It's unspoken, but you really can't say no to one of your regulars, otherwise they start taking you off the good accounts. So, for example, you've worked ten hours already, but one of your regulars wants to go to the Clippers game. He's a millionaire, and you know he's going to tip you like crazy, plus you don't want to lose the account. What can you do?"

"Why would a millionaire want to go to a Clippers game?" I ask.

"Because the billionaires take all the best seats at the Lakers games."

I can't argue with that logic, so I change the subject.

"You said this is your side hustle. What's your main hustle?"

"I'm an actor."

"Tough business," I say.

"The business is what it is, but it's the *craft* that keeps me coming back."

"How so?"

"I just like the script analysis, breaking down the character, getting inside of it," he says. "I know a lot of people come out to LA to be actors, but what they really want is to be famous. What they really want is to not have to work. But I like the work. I like trying to figure it out, finding a part of me that connects with the character to make something. But when you do make something, you have to be prepared to put it out into the universe and take whatever feedback comes your way."

"How do you mean?"

"Well, your favorite movie may not be my favorite movie, but ultimately those are just, like, opinions, man. If you're going to make something, you can't let the possibility of those opinions get into your head."

"What's your favorite movie?"

"Dude," the Lyft driver says. "*The Big Lebowski*. That's the greatest movie of all time."

"I can get you a toe," I say, "but you won't hear an argument from me on the masterpiece that is *The Big Lebowski*."

"You really tied the conversation together with that reference, dude."

"Of course, my mom thinks *The Big Lebowski* is dreck."

"What's dreck mean?" he asks.

"It's a Yiddish word that means trash or crap," I say. "She picked it up hanging out with Cynthia and Marty Ackerman."

"I feel like you should have a beverage for this ride," the Lyft driver says.

"You offered me a bottle of water when I got in, but I declined."

"I wish I had a white Russian for you."

"It'd be a lot cooler if you did."

"See, I'm not a fan of *Dazed and Confused*."

"No?"

"It feels real, which is great, but where's the story? What's the point?"

"I think the point is that there's a party at the moon tower."

"I need more," the Lyft driver says. "But I credit the actors in that movie for not thinking that it had to be more. They didn't worry that people would say, where the hell is the story? They just inhabited the world."

"I could be wrong, but I think the deleted scenes from that movie have a story," I say.

"Oh yeah?"

"Something about the decline of American masculinity after Vietnam and Pink's decision to play football in the fall. But they cut the Vietnam stuff, and so it was just this 'will he or won't he play,' but really it wasn't about that at all, it was just an endless parade of meaningless but highly quotable non-sequiturs."

"That's called reality," the Lyft driver says. "Look at Kanye meeting with Trump. What's the story there? It's not that Kanye is an insane genius, or that an artist at the top of the music industry is nuts. It's always been like that. Elvis was a freaking loon, but we didn't have to read his tweets."

"That's right!" I say. "Have you been to Graceland? He asked Nixon to make him an honorary FBI agent."

"Exactly," the Lyft driver says. "It's all just nonsense, and noise, and a big ball of crazy that's so insane you're supposed to drop everything and shit your pants. But it's also normal. The only new thing is that we watch it live. But there's no story there. Richard Linklater is just a poetic version of Mark Burnett."

"Yeah, but at least as far as we know Linklater is a good man, and thorough. I can't say the same for Burnett."

"No, dude, I'm pretty sure Burnett is a nihilist."

"Say what you will about the tenets of national socialism, dude, at least it's an ethos."

"Right," the Lyft driver says. "The Dude and Walter aren't just looking for the rug-pissers and a woman who probably kidnapped herself, they're pushing back against nihilism. Sure, they could be bowling, just hanging out with Smokey and talking about how that creep Quintana can roll, but that's not a movie. You need a story, something to push you forward. Otherwise, you're just hacking off toes, eating lingonberry pancakes, and passing out drunk in the pool, dreaming of your days in Autobahn and making *Logjammin'*—if, that is, you dream at all."

And just like that, we pull up to the North Hollywood Toyota dealership, which isn't far from the home of Larry Sellers on Radford, near the In-N-Out Burger.

"Thanks for the ride," I say. "My car has been in the shop all week, but if I had more Lyft drivers like you, I'd probably sell my car."

"Thanks, dude. But just FYI, I wouldn't hold out much hope for the Creedence."

14

OF MARRIAGE AND CATS

The Lyft driver just wants to go home.

"I forgot to turn off the app," he explains. "I was almost home, and then you were added to my queue."

He doesn't mean to make me feel guilty, but I can't help but think about the fact that after fighting traffic for an hour to drive me from Chatsworth to West Hollywood, the Lyft driver will spend the next hour fighting traffic, without a fare, trying to get home.

"I think this app will increase the divorce rate," he says. "My wife expects me home any minute, and now I'm going to West Hollywood. Maybe she thinks I'm cheating on her. I know a driver whose wife made him quit. She thinks he's cheating, always going here, going there. She thinks it's a cover for an affair, but that's the job. Then again, how does she know? Maybe he *is* cheating."

I'm not quite sure what to say, but then the Lyft driver laughs.

"I'm joking, of course," he says. "Not about my friend. His wife doesn't trust him, but that's their issue, not the app. I've been married fifty-two years. She trusts me. But at this point, even if we hated each other, even if we both cheated, what would be the point of getting divorced?"

"I don't know."

"Are you married?"

"Yes, seven years."

"Give yourself time, you'll understand."

"My older brother is single," he says. "He's seventy-eight. No wife. He had a heart attack recently."

"Is he OK?"

"Physically, yes. Everything else, he's a mess. He has nothing to live for, so he's very negative, and the negativity will kill him."

"Nothing to live for?"

"Nothing except three cats."

"Who took care of the cats while he was in the hospital?"

"His girlfriend."

I wonder if a girlfriend is worth living for. As if reading my thoughts, the Lyft driver answers my question.

"She loves the cats more than him. He loves the cats more than her. That's what they have in common."

We talk about how the traffic gets worse every year and how we blindly follow the mapping app, even though we know it makes dubious choices.

The Lyft driver tells me how he used to work for Pan Am in Iran, how he and his family fled after the revolution. He says careful observers will see evidence of the Iranian diaspora in every profession in Los Angeles, but especially law and medicine.

"We are at the top of every field."

He explains that he drives Lyft to keep busy.

"I find retirement boring."

We pass the time in traffic sharing snippets from our lives, but throughout the journey my mind keeps returning to his wife.

"You should call your wife and tell her you'll be late," I say.

"No need. After fifty-two years, she knows I'm always running late. Besides, she'll just tell me to stop at Trader Joe's."

We both chuckle.

"Your wife asks you to stop there too?" he asks.

"All the time."

"My secret is that I call her from Trader Joe's. That way she doesn't feel like she has to nag, that way it's like I'm thinking of her."

"You are thinking of her," I say.

"Exactly."

We hit a patch of bad traffic. The street lights are out on Sunset. It's stop and go, mostly stop.

"You couldn't go to your destination tomorrow night?" he jokes.

"No. I'm meeting my wife for dinner. It's her birth-day, and I promised that I'd drive her home."

The Lyft driver thinks about this for a moment.

"You said you were married seven years?"

"Yes?"

"You have cats?"

"No."

"You know more about life than my brother."

15

IMMIGRANT SONG

In the backseat of the Lyft, I spot what looks and smells like an ounce of weed in a sealed container. California voters legalized it, but I'm not sure the Lyft driver is complying with the spirit of the law, so I say, "Hey dude, do you realize you have a shit-ton of weed back here?"

"Oh yes," the Lyft driver says. "That is my weed."

On one level, I'm relieved because I don't have to contemplate the mechanics of a marijuana lost-and-found. *Can you describe your bud, sir?* But on another level, I'm concerned because he's driving, and my motto is safety first.

"I am not high," the Lyft driver assures me. "The weed is for ulcer."

"Weed works for ulcers?" I ask.

"It does nothing for ulcer," he says. "Weed is so I don't feel ulcer pain."

"Got it," I say. Then, looking at the weed, I add, "Either you're in a lot of pain, or you buy your weed at Costco."

The Lyft driver laughs.

"Pain," he says. "But there is discount for bulk. Plus, employee discount."

"From Lyft?"

"No, from dispensary where I work."

"So you work two jobs?" I ask.

"Three jobs," he says. "I Lyft. I sell weed at dispensary. I do sales for Boost Mobile. I love sales. I can sell ice to Eskimos."

"You sound like a hardworking dude."

"Oh, yes. I start selling shoes in Sri Lanka."

"Sri Lanka?"

"Yes, that is my home. I sell shoes. I taught myself English. I have an accent, and my grammar is fucked, but I learned English from TV."

"Most Americans don't know shit about grammar."

"Really?"

"Sure."

"Because I wonder, there is this punctuation . . . it looks like a comma and a period . . ."

"The semicolon."

"Semicolon. I do not understand this thing."

"You don't need it."

"Really?"

"Just use a period."

"How do you know?"

"I'm a writer. You don't need the semicolon; it's optional."

"Oh."

"Tell me about Sri Lanka," I say. "Do you miss it?"

"No. I miss my wife and daughter. I have not seen them in five years."

"Five years?"

"Yes."

"That must be hard."

"Very hard."

"Can you visit them?"

"No. I am bringing them here, but there is paperwork. I first came to the city of Connecticut. Do you know this place?"

"Yes."

"It is beautiful when the leaves change, but it is too cold."

"Agreed."

"There is a man, a powerful man who helps with the paperwork. His name is Blue Menthol."

"Blue Menthol?" I ask.

"Yes, Blue Menthol."

"You mean Senator Richard Blumenthal?"

"Yes, Blue Menthol. He helps with the paperwork because I am Muslim, and so it is dangerous for my family in Sri Lanka."

"Are your wife and daughter safe?"

"Before I leave, I move them to safe place. But there is always violence there. The country is Buddhist, and they do not like the Muslims. There was civil war. But even today, there is violence. I was almost blown up."

"Really?"

"Yes, my school blew up. I was across the street."

"You're lucky."

"Very lucky," he says. "Where my wife and daughter live, someone kill a Buddhist man, so they blame the Muslims. Then people make bombs out of bottles with gasoline."

"Molotov cocktails."

"Yes."

"And they throw these bombs into Muslim homes. One hundred and twenty people killed."

"Jesus."

"Yes, Jesus."

"But your wife and daughter are OK?"

"Yes. But they cannot be Muslims in Sri Lanka. Every religion has a way to do things. Like we eat halal. Do you know this?"

"Yeah, it's like keeping Kosher."

"Exactly. You are a bad Muslim if you don't eat halal. Or if you smoke weed. I am a bad Muslim. I like the bacon. I smoke the weed."

"Hey, you gotta live your truth."

"Yes. But in Sri Lanka, the Buddhists say the Muslims can't do this, can't do that. It's not safe to be a Muslim, you understand?"

"I do."

"So, that is why I come here. That is why I work three jobs. That is why I call Blue Menthol."

"Do you think that's why you have an ulcer?"

"No. America is opportunity, not ulcer."

ABOUT THE AUTHOR

Michael Estrin lives, writes, and rides in Los Angeles. His creative nonfiction has appeared in Narratively, Tablet, and Vox. To learn more about him and to hear about upcoming books, please visit:

www.mestrin.com

Made in the USA
Las Vegas, NV
15 November 2020